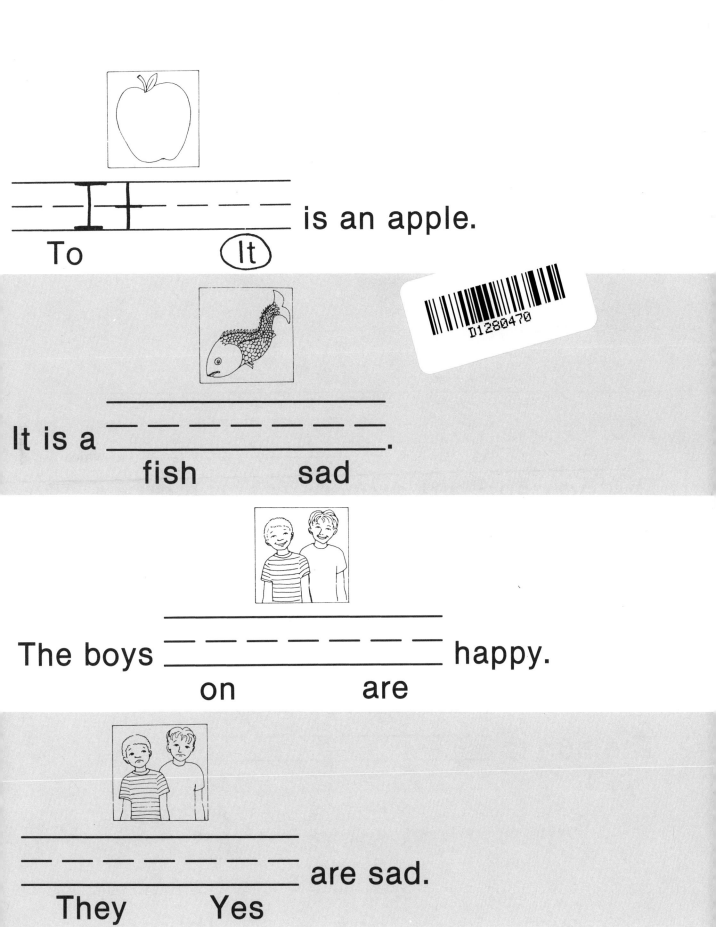

___It___ is an apple.

To   (It)

It is a _____.

fish   sad

The boys _____ happy.

on   are

_____ are sad.

They   Yes

The boy and girl are playing. They run and jump on the slide. Then they go fishing. The sun is hot, but the boy and girl are happy.

The boy and girl are _happy_.

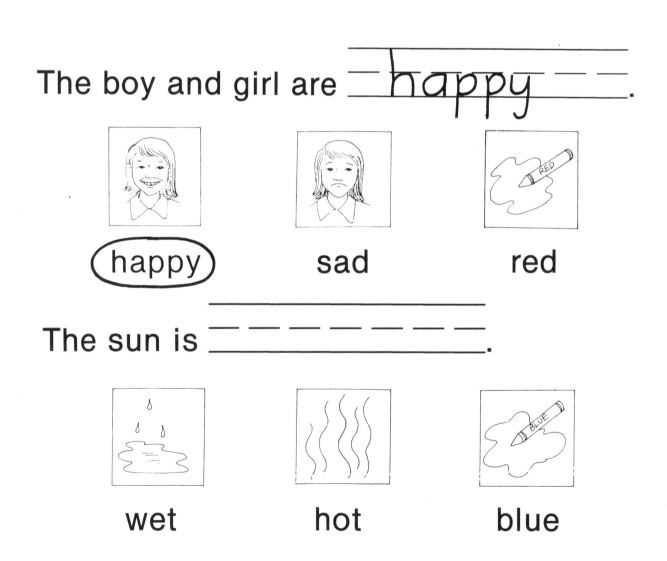

happy   sad   red

The sun is _____.

wet   hot   blue

Mom and dad are going to eat it. It is in a pan. It is not a fish and it is not a hot dog. It is red.

It is *meat*.

hot dog

(meat)

fish

It is meat.

They can sit.

girl   tree

fish   red

boy   Dad

1. 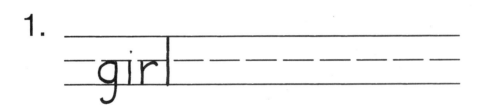 girl

2. 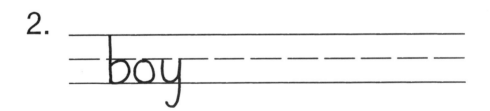 boy

3.  Dad

It is a _____.

pin   fish

It is a _____.

hole   they

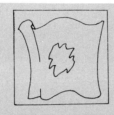

Mom _____,"Go to bed."

up   said

Dad _____ ,"Look at the hole."

at   says

5

Dad looks at the hole in the blue rug.

He says, "It's a big hole, but I can pin it."

Dad pins the hole. Then the rug looks good, so Dad is happy.

_____

The rug is _____.

big	blue	red

The hole is _____.

blue	rug	big

You can go up it. You can sit on it.
You slide down it. You play on it. It is not
a tree.

It is a _____.

tree

apple

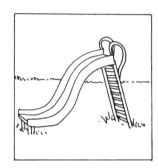
slide

They can run.

hole   cat

Mom   pin

dog   mud

1. _____

2. _____

3. _____

The fish is in the _____.

pin   lake

The _____ is yellow and fuzzy.

bee   hole

The jet can _____.

fly   it

The bees fly to the _____.

too   lake

9

A yellow and black bee is sitting in the mud. A little boy is playing in the grass. Then the boy slides in the mud and sits on the bee.

He jumps up. "It's a bee! I sat on a bee!" he says.

The bee is in the _____.

hole

slide

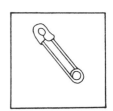
mud

The boy sat on a _____.

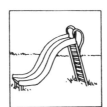
bee

slide

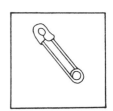
pin

He is little. He can run, play, and go fishing. He can eat pizza, too. He can jump, but he can not fly.

_____

He is a _____.

bee

boy

dog

_____

_____

A boy can eat it.

hole

lake

pizza

egg

hot dog

dog

1. _____

2. _____

3. _____

The jets _____ up.

fly   lake

The cats _____ playing.

zip   are

The pin is in a _____.

look   dress

The _____ is on the pan.

fly   said

Pat and Dad are going fishing. They are going to Blue Lake. Pat says to Dad, "Are the fish in Blue Lake big?"

Dad says, "No, they are little."

Then Pat is happy to fish.

The fish are _____ _____.

big   little   blue

The lake is _____ _____.

big   little   blue

They are little, and they are yellow and black. They can fly to a lake or to a tree. They can eat, but they can not jump or run.

_____

They are _____.

bees

girls

jets

_____

_____

They can jump.

girl

hill

boy

apple

Dad

tub

1. _____

2. _____

3. _____

Mom eats _____.

jam   are

Pat plays _____ Mom.

with   fly

Dad says, " _____ can jump."

Pin   You

The _____ is on the lake.

duck   bee

A black tub is on the hill. Six little yellow ducks are playing in it.

Then a cat runs up to the tub. The cat jumps in the tub with the ducks, and so the ducks fly up to the tree.

The ducks fly to the _____.

tub

tree

cat

The ducks are _____.

black

yellow

fishing

It is red. It is sweet, but it is not an apple. You can eat it, but it is not meat.

_____

It is _____.

jam   an apple   meat

_____

_____

You can sit on it.

yellow

rug

with

bed

sad

slide

1. _____

2. _____

3. _____

20

The _____ is flying.

     bee   bird

The _____ is yellow.

     nest   jam

The _____ is green.

    grass   duck

The bird is in the _____.

       with   nest

The boy saw a nest up in a tree. He said to the girl, "Look at the nest!"

The girl looked up at the nest. "See the little black bird sleeping in the nest?" she asked.

The boy saw a _____.

  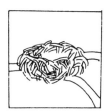

bird　　　　grass　　　　nest

The girl saw a _____.

Dad　　　　bird　　　　saw

A bird sleeps in it, but it is not a bed.
It is grass, but it is not green. It is in a tree.

_____

It is a _____.

grass

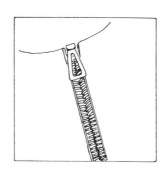
zip

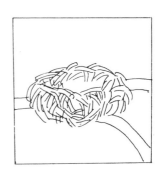
nest

_____
_ _ _ _ _ _ _ _ _ _ _ _ _ _
_____

_____
_ _ _ _ _ _ _ _ _ _ _ _ _ _
_____

They can fly.

bird   nest

jet   bee

jam   grass

1. _____

2. _____

3. _____

The birds _____ in the mud.

you   dig

Pat digs in the _____.

bird   sand

The boy plays in a _____ box.

sand   nest

The girls _____ a sand box.

make   grass

Pat is playing in a big red sand box. She makes a hill with the sand. Then she digs a hole in the hill. She runs and jumps in the hole.

Then Pat goes and sits on the grass in the sun and sleeps.

Pat makes a _ _ _ _ _ _ _ _.

box

grass

hill

Pat jumps in the _ _ _ _ _ _ _ _.

hole

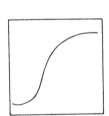
grass

box

It is little. It can dig in the grass and eat. It can make a nest, and it can fly, too. It is not a bee.

It is a _____.

jet   dog   bird

They are green.

pizza

grass

tree

sun

sand

green rug

1. _____

2. _____

3. _____

Pat can _____ in the sand.

        they   dig

_____ can eat jam.

   You   make

The bird makes a _____.

        nest   lake

Dad _____ a cap.

   sand   made

The girl has a duck. It is yellow and fuzzy. She pats her fuzzy little duck. But the duck runs into the mud. Then the duck is wet, not fuzzy.

"You are too wet to pat," says the girl.

The duck is too _____.

fuzzy

wet

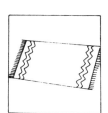
little

The duck is _____.

big

red

yellow

It is big. Grass is on it. You can run up it. You can sit on it and sleep on it, too. A bus can go on it.

It is a _____.

bed

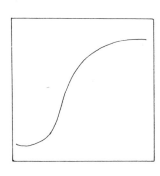
hill

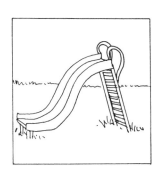
slide

They can go fishing.

boy

jam

Mom

girl

pan

apple

1. _____

         - - - - - - - - - - - - - - -

         _____

2. _____

         - - - - - - - - - - - - - - -

         _____

3. _____

         - - - - - - - - - - - - - - -

         _____

The boy is _____.

bird   Sandy

Sandy said, "I _____ jumping."

duck   am

He said, "It is _____ to play."

jam   fun

He said, "Look at _____."

me   are

Mom said to Sandy, "I am going to the lake. Are you going with me?"

Sandy said, "Yes, I'll go with you. It is fun to go to the lake."

Sandy is _____.

sad

fun

happy

They are going to the _____.

lake

sand box

bed

It is green. You can sit on it and you can jump on it, too. It is not a box or a bed. You can cut it.

_____

It is _____.

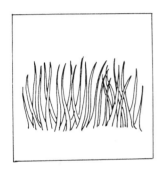
grass

mud

six

_____

_____

They can eat.

sand

duck

tub

boy

bird

box

1. _____

2. _____

3. _____

They are playing a _____.

game   me

The bus can _____.

dug   stop

The _____ is blue.

ball   with

The ball _____ is fun.

game   am

Pat and Sandy are playing in the grass.

They are playing a game with six balls.

Pat digs a hole in the mud. Then

Sandy slides the balls into the hole. Pat

and Sandy are having fun.

They have six _____.

boys

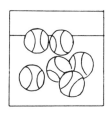
balls

girls

Pat digs in the _____.

mud

grass

lake

It is fun. You can play it. Girls and boys can play it. Dads and moms can play it, too.

_____

It is a _____.

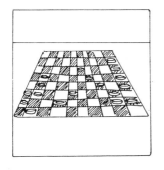  

game   cut   zip

_____

_____

They are fun.

sad duck

playing

game

hot pan

egg

ball

1. _____

2. _____

3. _____

Dad is in a _____.

       ball   car

The car is a _____.

       toy   you

The boys _____ on the ducks.

       ride   fish

Sandy rides in the toy _____.

       me   car

The toy car is on the grass. A blue bird flies to the little red car. Then the bird sits in it.

Sun sees the bird in the car. She says, "Look! The bird is having a ride in the car!"

The bird is in the _____.

car   grass   tree

The car is a _____.

 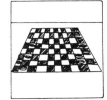 

toy   game   bus

Boys can play with it. Girls can play with it, too. They can play games with it.

It is fun to play with. It is not a dog or cat.

It is a ＿＿＿＿＿＿＿.

hole

toy

bee

They are toys.

play car

toy jet

me

Dad's car

school

play bus

1. _____

2. _____

3. _____

Sandy said, "_____ the dog!"
Stop   Game

They _____ in the car.
ride   fun

The _____ game is fun.
stop   ball

Pat plays with the _____.
car   toy

Mom made a green and blue dress for Sun. Sun has the dress on. Mom zips it up.

"The dress looks good on you, Sun," she says. "It is not too big."

Sun is happy with her new dress.

The dress is — — — — — — — —.

Sun's

Mom's

on the grass

Sun is — — — — — — —.

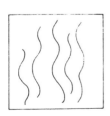
hot

happy

sad

It is big. You can sit in it. You can ride in it, too. It can stop and go. It is not a toy, and it is not a car.

It is a _____.

fish

bus

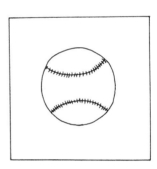
ball

They can go.

jet   bus

dress   black

tree   car

1. _____

2. _____

3. _____

The fish _____.
swim   grass

Sandy is _____ at the cat.
fun   mad

Dad said, " _____ dog."
Good   Sand

_____ is a boy.
Ball   Carlos

Carlos goes to the lake with Dad.

Dad and Carlos play ball, but it is too

hot, so they go swimming.

"I'm not hot if I'm in the lake, Dad.

Are you?" asks Carlos.

Dad and Carlos have a _____.

fish

ride

swim

It is too _____ to play.

mad

fun

hot

It swims in the lake. It can not fly or run. You can eat it. It is not a duck.

It is a _____.

fish   duck   bee

They can swim.

pizza

fish

game

Mom

Dad

saw

1. _____

2. _____

3. _____

Carlos looks at _____.

swim   T.V.

The _____ is yellow.

Carlos   house

The little _____ digs.

good   puppy

The _____ is in the dog house.

puppy   mad

Sun made a hot dog. She was going to eat it and read her book.

She sat down with the hot dog. Sun was looking at her book and not at the hot dog. Her little puppy jumped up and took the hot dog. Sun had to make an egg to eat.

Sun made an _____.

apple

egg

pizza

The puppy took the _____.

book

hot dog

toy dog

It is big and wet, and it is blue. Fish swim in it. You can swim in it, too. It is not a tub.

_____

It is a _____.

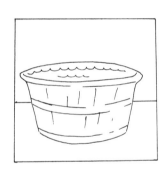

lake　　　　　mud　　　　　tub

_____

_____

_____

_____

They are in a house.

grass

rug

bed

tree

lake

jam

1. _____
   - - - - - - - - - - - -
   _____

2. _____
   - - - - - - - - - - - -
   _____

3. _____
   - - - - - - - - - - - -
   _____

The _____ is wet.
T.V.   mop

The boy plays with a _____.
friend   dog

Mom said, "It is _____ you."
ride   for

Dad can _____ the house.
toy   mop

The rug has jam on it. Mom says to Carlos, "Look at the jam on the rug! Can you mop it up for me?"

Carlos mops up the jam for Mom, so Mom is happy.

Carlos mops up the ＿＿＿＿＿＿＿.

jam

can

mud

Mom is ＿＿＿＿＿＿＿.

sad

mad

happy

It can sit, and it can run. It can dig holes in the mud, too. It is fun to play with. It is little, but it is not a cat.

_____

It is a _____.

mop   cat   puppy

_____

_ _ _ _ _ _ _ _ _ _ _ _ _ _ _ _ _

_____

_ _ _ _ _ _ _ _ _ _ _ _ _ _ _ _ _

They can have friends.

mop

Carlos

toy

boy

jam

girl

1. _____

2. _____

3. _____

The girl _____ a friend.
has   for

Carlos is _____ at the puppy.
mad   mop

The T.V. is in the _____.
house   puppy

Eggs are _____ for you.
friend   good

Pat had a little puppy. She said, "I can make a dog house for the puppy." So she made a dog house. She made a little rug for the dog house, too.

Then Pat said, "The puppy has a good house."

Pat made the dog _____.

sit

house

run

She made a little _____.

toy dog

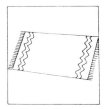
rug

duck

It is big. Mom and Dad can sit in it, but it is not a house. It is not a car or a bus. It can fly.

It is a _____.

bee

house

jet

They can dig.

T.V.

puppy

sun

can

dog

Dad

1. _____

2. _____

3. _____

The girls _____.

fall   hole

Carlos runs _____ the hill.

down   up

The meat is in a _____.

for   bag

The pen _____ in the hole.

said   fell

Dad has six eggs in a bag. The bag is on the car. The cat jumps into the bag. "Stop it, cat!" says Dad, but the bag falls down. The eggs fall on the grass. Dad is mad!

_____

The eggs fall on the _____.

grass

car

cat

Dad has six _____.

cats

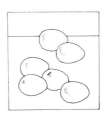
eggs

cars

It can run up a tree. It can run down a hill. It can jump up on a car, too. It can eat and it can sleep, but it can not fly.

_____

It is a $_____$.

bird   bee   cat

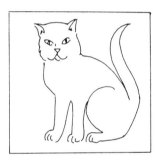

_____

_____

They can play with you.

boy   friend

girl   bag

down   egg

1. _____
   _ _ _ _ _ _ _ _ _ _ _ _ _ _ _
   _____

2. _____
   _ _ _ _ _ _ _ _ _ _ _ _ _ _ _
   _____

3. _____
   _ _ _ _ _ _ _ _ _ _ _ _ _ _ _
   _____

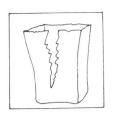

The bag has a _____ in it.

rip   fall

The _____ is for Dad.

down   cake

Ran Pin can _____.

see   fall

Sandy sees the _____.

cake   at

Pat has a cake for Mom. She stops to play on the see-saw with a friend. The cake is on the grass, and Pat is on the see-saw. Pat falls down and slides into the cake. She is so sad!

Pat plays with a _____.

friend

saw

Mom

Pat is _____.

sad

mad

happy

You can have eggs or toys in it. A cat can sleep in it, but it is not a bed or a box.

_____

It is a _____.

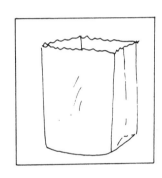

pin   bag   duck

_____
_ _ _ _ _ _ _ _ _ _ _ _ _ _ _ _
_____

_____
_ _ _ _ _ _ _ _ _ _ _ _ _ _ _ _
_____

You can rip it.

bag   cap

mud   sun

dress   pen

1. _____

2. _____

3. _____

The _____ is red.

  rip   bat

The _____ is wet.

  see   milk

The _____ is Dad's.

  cake   cup

The milk is in the _____.

  cup   toy

Sun is at bat. She is looking at the ball. The ball goes up.

Sun bats the ball, and it goes into the lake.

Sun runs and runs.

Sun looks at the _____.

lake

bat

ball

Sun bats the ball into the _____.

mud

lake

sand

It can fly, but it is not a jet. It can swim in the lake, but it is not a fish. It is fuzzy.

_____

It is a _____.

bee

cup

duck

_____
_ _ _ _ _ _ _ _ _ _ _ _ _ _ _ _ _ _ _
_____

_____
_ _ _ _ _ _ _ _ _ _ _ _ _ _ _ _ _ _ _
_____

They are wet.

T.V.

milk

lake

bat

mud

rug

1. _____

2. _____

3. _____

_____
_ _ _ _ _ _ _ _
_____ is good for you.
   Milk   Cup

The boy is at _____.
        bag   bat

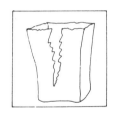

The _____ has a rip.
   bag   see

The cup fell _____.
      bat   down

Carlos is taking a cup of milk to Dad. He can't see the puppy sleeping on the rug. Carlos falls down on the puppy, and the puppy jumps up. The milk is on Carlos, not in the cup!

The milk falls on _____.

the puppy

the rug

Carlos

The puppy naps on _____.

Dad

Carlos

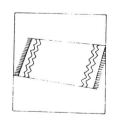
the rug

It is brown and wet. Ducks can sit in it. Little boys and girls can play in it. And dogs can dig in it.

_____

It is _____.

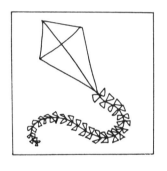
a kite

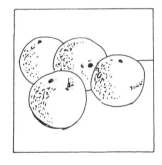
oranges

mud

_____

_____

They are little.

house

pin

jet

bird

big lake

pen

1. _____

2. _____

3. _____

Ran Pin eats a _____.
                    am   roll

Dad _____ eating cake.
      roll   was

The _____ was black.
     six   ten

The _____ is red.
     bike   rip

Ran Pin is sitting on the hill eating pizza. The hill has apple trees on it. An apple falls down and rolls to Ran Pin. He says, "I think I'll eat an apple, too."

Ran Pin is on the ＿＿＿＿＿＿＿.

tree   apple   hill

The hill has a ＿＿＿＿＿＿＿ on it.

tree   roll   bike

A boy or girl can ride on it. It is fun to ride. You can make it stop and go, and you can ride it up hills. It is not a bus.

It is a _____.

milk   bat   bike

They can ride bikes.

roll

pizza

Dad

bee

boy

girl

1. _____

2. _____

3. _____

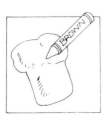

The roll is _____.

black   brown

The bike is _____.

fat   orange

It is a cup _____ milk.

of   was

It is a bag _____ pins.

ten   of

Sandy and Ran Pin are on bikes. Sandy has a bag of oranges. The boys stop their bikes at the park. They take the bag and sit on the grass to eat their oranges.

The bag has _____ in it.

bikes

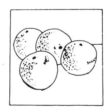

oranges

Sandy

The boys stop to _____.

bike

fish

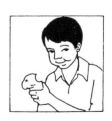

eat

It is brown. You can make it in a pan. You can have it hot. You can eat it with jam.

_____

It is a _____.

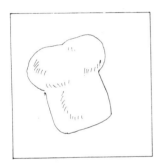

roll   bike   pan

_____

_____

They are brown.

nest

sun

mud

orange

puppy

blue

1. _____

2. _____

3. _____

The _____ is orange.
    brown   kite

Boys and girls go to _____.
                  school   of

The _____ is brown.
    orange   coat

The coat is in _____.
               school   bike

Sun and Pat are on the school bus. They have their coats on, and they have their school bags in their laps.

"I'm going to put my coat in my school bag," says Sun. Then the bus stops at school. The girls go into school, but Sun's school bag is on the bus—and so is her coat!

The girls ride on the _ _ _ _ _ _ _.

 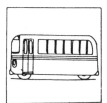 

coats   bus   apple

The girls are going to _ _ _ _ _ _ _.

the bus stop   school   the house

You can play with it. You can bat it. You can run with it. It can go up and down, and it can roll. It is not a toy.

It is a _____.

ball   toy   game

They are in school.

kite

girls

boys

pens

puppy

house

1. _____

   — — — — — — — — — —

   _____

2. _____

   — — — — — — — — — —

   _____

3. _____

   — — — — — — — — — —

   _____

The _____ is at school.

bike   kite

Carlos has an _____ coat.

orange   roll

It is a box _____ oranges.

coat   of

The _____ is brown.

school   kite

Sandy and Carlos have a red and orange kite. They take it up on a hill. They run so the kite can go up. A tree makes a little hole in the kite, but it can not stop the kite. Sandy and Carlos are happy the kite can fly.

The kite is on a _____.

fly

hill

hole

The kite has a _____ in it.

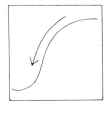

hill

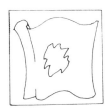

hole

tree

You can eat it, but it is not a roll. It is red, but it is not meat or pizza. It is good for you.

_____

It is an _____.

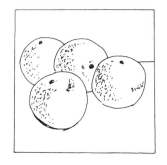

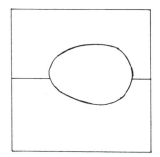

oranges   apple   egg

_____

_ _ _ _ _ _ _ _ _ _ _ _ _ _ _ _ _

_____

_ _ _ _ _ _ _ _ _ _ _ _ _ _ _ _ _

Here are some of the words that are introduced in this book:

bag	ball	bat	bee	bike
bird	brown	cake	car	coat
cup	dig/dug	down	duck	fall/fell
fish	fly	friend	game	grass
hole	house	jam	kite	lake